Challenging
Coin
Puzzles

by Terry Stickels

Scholastic Inc.

New York   Toronto   London   Auckland   Sydney
Mexico City   New Delhi   Hong Kong   Buenos Aires

ISBN 0-439-38879-1

12 11 10 9 8 7 6 5 4 3 2 1   3 4 5 6 7 8/0

Printed in the U.S.A.   40
First printing, April 2003

Introduction

Challenging Coin Puzzles contains every type of coin puzzle imaginable. From tic-tac-toe with nickels and dimes to sliding coin puzzles to a coin-filled word search, get ready for a challenge!

Some puzzles are more challenging than others. Just remember — don't become discouraged if a puzzle stumps you. You can always skip it and go back to it later. Sometimes solving one puzzle will help you solve others.

Are you ready for the challenge? Turn the page!

Easy Coin Puzzles

1. Here are nine pennies arranged in a triangle. Here's the challenge — change the positions of two coins to turn the triangle into a square.

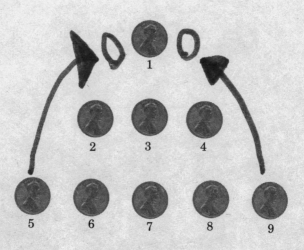

2. Beth flipped a nickel five times. Each time, the nickel landed heads-up. The challenge is to figure out the chances of the nickel landing heads-up when Beth flips it for the sixth time.

3. Let's play tic-tac-toe with nickels and dimes! Below is the start of a game in which the nickel has moved first. It's your turn. The challenge is to place your dime in the only square that will stop the nickel from winning the game.

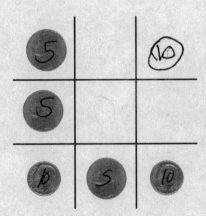

4. Read the poem below. The challenge is to come up with the total value of all the coins.

> Nickels and dimes, I have some.
> Add in some quarters to make it more fun.
> Four of the first — now, that's just a start.
> Six of the dimes — but that's only part.
> Half of the sum of the numbers above
> Will give you the quarters I know you just love.
> So tell me, my friends, what do you see?
> How much money for you and for me?

5. Here's a word search for you. The challenge is to find the words ~~cents~~, ~~change~~, ~~coins~~, ~~currency~~, ~~dime~~, ~~dollar~~, ~~money~~, ~~nickel~~, ~~penny~~, puzzle, and ~~quarter~~. They can be up, down, diagonal, or backward.

done

```
Q U A R T E P E N N R O
U D N F E Q D I M E Z A
A I I S O L M Y T O P Q
R Y C N U R Q R D I M A
T N K I W P A L L O D B
E N I O E U I L N I C K
O E Q C Q Z D O L L A D
C P M N K A C I N O E I
E L I E R E A L L O D M
N Z D P D O L L A C I A
L R Q P A O S K R N D I
E G N A H C L B F G K Z
Q M T R L F C D N L U W
S R O V E A M I K C E G
T U J N F P L O P N T Q
N U A P E W R M N P R B
E L Z Z U P T N B E S F
C U R R E N C Y D L Y G
```

5

6. Here are six dimes arranged in a triangle.

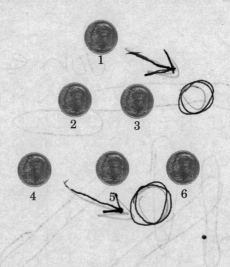

Here's the challenge — turn this triangle upside down by changing the positions of only two coins.

7. Olivia needed change for the bus. She exchanged three one-dollar bills for nickels and dimes and received the exact same number of nickels as dimes. The challenge is to figure out how many nickels there were in the change.

8. Here's the challenge — how many quarters are there in $25.00?

   a. 10
   b. 100
   c. 1,000
   d. 48

9. The U.S. Mint is where American coins are made, or "minted." The headquarters are in Washington, D.C., and there are four other locations throughout the United States.

Below are five cities. Only one of these cities does not mint coins. The challenge is to figure out which city doesn't belong.

a. Dallas, Texas
b. Denver, Colorado
c. Philadelphia, Pennsylvania
d. San Francisco, California
e. West Point, New York

10. Here's the challenge — take four of the same type of coin and arrange them so that each coin is touching the other three coins.

11. Without looking, name the presidents who appear on a penny, nickel, dime, and quarter.

abraham   washington

12. If one cent is equal to one second, how much money would you have after two and a half minutes?

150¢

1.50¢

9

Medium Coin Puzzles

13. Here's some fun trivia to challenge you. How many pennies would you have to stack on top of one another in order for the height of your pile of pennies to equal the diameter of one penny?

14. Below you'll find a list of five different coins. To the right of this list are the countries that issue these coins — but not in the correct order. Here's the challenge — match each coin with its correct country.

1. bolivar   a. India
2. yen   b. Switzerland
3. krona   c. Sweden
4. rupee   d. Japan
5. franc   e. Venezuela

15. Here's a fun puzzle called "numlets," where the questions have numbers and letters. The challenge is to figure out what phrase is represented by the letters and numbers. Here are two examples:

There are 2 N in a D.
The answer is, "There are two nickels in a dime."

Here's another example:
There are 25 P in a Q.
The answer is, "There are twenty-five pennies in a quarter."

Can you solve the numlets below?

a. There are 10 N in a HD.
b. There are 5 P and 2 D in a Q.
c. There are 5 P and 1 N in a D.

16. Here's a challenge — using nine pennies, arrange them to make five squares. (The squares do not have to be the same size.)

17. Hidden in the paragraph below are the names of three American coins. Can you find them?

Elise was worried. Because of the poor lighting in the dim entry of the ballroom, her worst fears were about to happen: nylons torn and broken heels. Her date was about to nick electrical wires that were sticking out from a light fixture, but Elise pulled him away at the last second.

18. Margaret spent 75¢ on two pieces of candy. One of the candies cost 35¢ more than the other. The challenge is to figure out how much each piece of candy costs.

19. Mark won a penny-counting contest. He was given 8 pennies on the first day, 88 pennies on the second day, and 888 pennies on the third day. Here's the challenge — how many pennies did Mark average over the three days?

20. Molly has 73¢, Alex has 29¢, and Coley has 45¢. Molly says to Alex and Coley, "If we add up our three coin amounts and divide by three, we will all have the same amount of money."

Alex asked Molly how she figured that out so quickly. Molly said, "I know a trick that will tell me if any whole number is evenly divisible by three."

The challenge is to figure out Molly's trick.

21. From a pile of fifty pennies, fifty nickels, and fifty dimes, choose sixteen coins that have a value of exactly 50¢. You must use at least one penny, one nickel, and one dime.

22. How many words can you make from the letters in the word *quarter*? The challenge is to find at least twelve.

23. Using four nickels and four dimes, place all the coins in a 4 x 4 grid so that no two coins of the same denomination are next to each other horizontally, vertically, or diagonally. Here's the answer that's usually given:

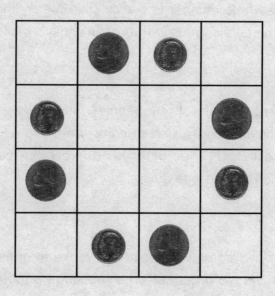

Can you come up with at least one different solution?

24. An analogy is a kind of word puzzle. First, figure out the relationship of the first two words in the puzzle. Then look for an answer in the second part of the puzzle that will keep the same relationship. Here's an example:

white : black : : day : ?

This reads as, "White is to black as day is to __?" The answer, of course, is "night." Here's another example:

bicycle : 2 : : car : ?

This reads as, "Bicycle is to two as car is to __?" A bicycle has two wheels and a car has four. Four is the correct answer.

Solve these coin analogies.

a. 1 : 5 : : dime : ?
b. 2 : 5 : : dime : ?
c. 1 : 5 : : penny : ?
d. 5 : 10 : : Jefferson : ?

Hard Coin Puzzles

25. Here's the challenge — figure out how much money you would have if you took one fifth of one half of one seventh of 70¢.

26. Sasha has two coins in her pocket. She knows that at least one of the coins is a dime. She knows that the other coin is either a dime or a nickel. What are the chances that both coins are dimes? Be careful with this puzzle — the answer may surprise you!

27. I have two coins that total 35¢. One of the coins is not a dime. The challenge is to figure out what the two coins are.

28. If you have the same amount of pennies and nickels and no other coins, one of the money amounts below is the only possibility of the total amount you could have. What's the correct answer?

    a. 49¢
    b. 91¢
    c. 36¢
    d. 45¢

29. Would you rather have a job that pays you $2,500 a month or a job where you are paid 1¢ on the first day, 2¢ on the second day, 4¢ on the third day, 8¢ on the fourth day, and so on for a month?

30. Martha has 41¢ in coins. No two coins have the same value. How many coins does Martha have?

31. A penny, nickel, dime, and quarter are arranged in a straight line. From the clues below, figure out the order the coins appear in from left to right.

- The quarter is next to the nickel and the dime.
- The nickel is not last.
- The dime is next to the penny.

32. Andy, Brenda, and Curt compared the amount of change each had at the bottoms of their backpacks. They learned that Andy and Brenda together had 12¢, Brenda and Curt together had 18¢, and Andy and Curt together had 10¢. Here's the challenge — who had the least amount of money and how much did that person have?

33. During last semester, Mindy's parents gave her a quarter for each A she received on a science test. For any grade lower than an A, Mindy had to give her parents a dime. At the end of the semester, Mindy had 80¢. There were six total tests, and the teacher only gave solid letter grades. How many A's did Mindy receive?

34. Here's a fun game to try with family and friends. Take ten pennies and arrange them like so:

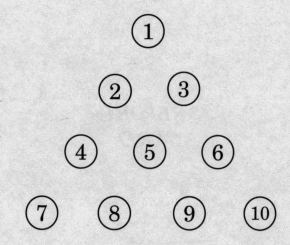

Next, remove penny number 8 to make a space. Now the remaining pennies can "jump" over one another.

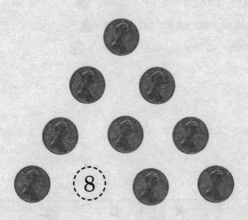

The challenge in this game is to jump the pennies one at a time so there is only one penny left. The jumps are just like checkers — jump one coin over another and into an empty space. Then remove the penny that was just jumped over.

Here's the first move: Move penny number 10 over penny number 9 so that it lands in the empty spot left by penny number 8. Now remove penny number 9.

Good luck!

35. Below are five cards that represent different combinations of two coins each.

A penny is represented by a ★
A nickel is represented by a ●
A dime is represented by a ▲
A quarter is represented by a ■

The five cards look like this:

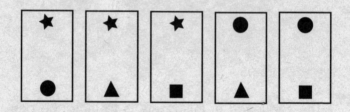

There's one card missing in the series. Here's the challenge — figure out what two symbols should be on the sixth card.

36. A group of students contributed $1.21 toward purchasing special ribbon for a class project. Each student paid his or her share with the same two coins. The challenge is to figure out how many total dimes were contributed. Here's a hint: What number divides evenly into $1.21?

Challenging Coin Puzzles

37. A total of thirteen pennies is put into three piles so that each pile has a different number of pennies. Obviously, this can be done in several ways. Here's the challenge — what is the fewest possible number of pennies in the largest pile of any of the possible combinations?

38. Bill has four pennies to place in three cups of the same size. He must place an odd number of coins in each cup. The challenge is to figure out how this can be done.

39. What is the most change you can have and not be able to make change for a nickel, dime, or quarter?

40. Aman has one penny, two nickels, one dime, and two quarters in his pocket. He takes out two coins and writes down the sum of their values and then puts them back with the other coins. He continues taking out two coins at a time, writing the sum of their values and putting them back. Here's the challenge — how many different sums can Aman record?

41. A mother has two children who want bubble gum from a penny gumball machine. The children want the same color gum. There are three different-colored gumballs — red, green, and yellow. How many pennies will the mother have to put into the gumball machine to make sure that the children get gumballs of the same color?

42. Two of the three statements below are false. Here's the challenge — figure out who has a quarter and who has a dime.

- Bill has a quarter.
- Bill has a dime.
- Bob has a dime.

43. Two mothers and three daughters found six coins on a walk. They split the coins evenly among them. How was this possible?

44. Take six coins of any amount and lay them on a flat surface. Here's the challenge — give yourself a minute and see if you can arrange these six coins so there are three coins in each of three different straight lines.

45. Marcia and her friend Kathy were walking home from school. Marcia said, "If you can answer my riddle, I'll buy us both an ice-cream cone."

Here's Marcia's riddle: "I have several coins in my pocket. All but two are quarters, all but two are dimes, and all but two are pennies. How many coins do I have?"

Kathy answered correctly, and then said, "I hope you have more money than that or neither of us will have an ice-cream cone!" Marcia had a $5 bill, and they both enjoyed their cone.

Here's the challenge — how many coins did Marcia have?

46. You have six coins that all appear identical. One of the six coins weighs less than the others, but you can't tell by just looking. Using a balance scale, the challenge is to determine which coin is the lightest in just two weighings.

47. Robert told his brother that he could put nine quarters in two rows in such a way that each row will have five quarters. Robert's brother said it couldn't be done. The challenge is to show Robert's brother that he's wrong.

48. John's teacher asked the class to take out a sheet of paper and write down the answer to this question:

How much money would you have if you added 1¢ plus 2¢ plus 3¢, and so on, all the way to 20¢?

Without writing anything, John quickly answered, "$2.10." He was right! How did John figure out the answer to this question so quickly?

Here's a hint: Everyone has the ability to solve this puzzle as quickly as John did. You just have to think about it in a different way.

Answer Key

1.

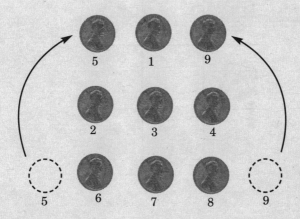

Move coins 5 and 9 as indicated. The triangle is now a square!

2. The chances are one out of two. Although it may seem unusual for a coin to land heads-up five times in a row, the chances still remain the same for each individual flip. Since every coin has two sides, the chance of it landing on either side is always one out of two.

3. Here's where you should place the dime:

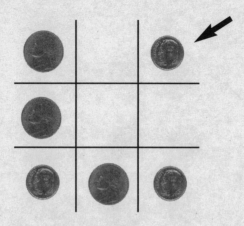

Not only will this move stop the nickel from winning, but the dime is now in a position where it will win no matter where the nickel moves next!

4. There are four nickels, which are worth 20¢. Six dimes are worth 60¢. There are ten total coins, and one half of ten is five. That means there are five quarters, which are worth $1.25. When you add 20¢ + 60¢ + $1.25, you'll find that the total of the coins is $2.05.

5.

```
Q U A R T E P E N N R O
U D N F E Q D I M E Z A
A I I S O L M Y T O P Q
R Y C N U R Q R D I M A
T N K I W P A L L O D B
E N I O E U I L N I C K
O E Q C Q Z D O L L A D
C P M N K A C I N O E I
E L I E R E A L L O D M
N Z D P D O L L A C I A
L R Q P A O S K R N D I
E G N A H C L B F G K Z
Q M T R L F C D N L U W
S R O V E A M I K C E G
T U J N F P L O P N T Q
N U A P E W R M N P R B
E L Z Z U P T N B E S F
C U R R E N C Y D L Y G
```

6. Move coins one and four. The triangle is now upside down!

Can you come up with another way to solve this puzzle?

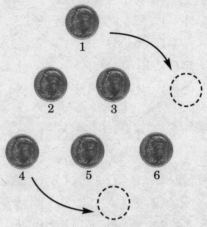

7. Olivia received twenty nickels in the change. Twenty nickels are worth $1.00 and twenty dimes are worth $2.00.

8. b. There are 100 quarters in $25.00.

9. a. Dallas, Texas, is the only city on the list that does not mint coins.

10. Here's how to do it:

The coin in the middle rests on top of the other three coins.

11. Abraham Lincoln appears on the penny; Thomas Jefferson appears on the nickel; Franklin Roosevelt appears on the dime; George Washington appears on the quarter.

12. You would have $1.50. There are 120 seconds in two minutes and 30 seconds in one half of a minute. Since each second equals one cent, 120 seconds + 30 seconds = 150 seconds, or $1.50.

13. Approximately twelve and a half pennies stacked on top of one another is equal to the diameter of one penny.

14. 1. e; 2. d; 3. c; 4. a; 5. b

15. a. There are ten nickels in a half-dollar.
    b. There are five pennies and two dimes in a quarter.
    c. There are five pennies and one nickel in a dime.

16.

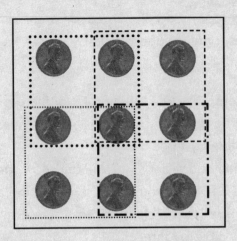

17. The hidden coins are in boldface below.

Elise was worried. Because of the poor lighting in the **dim e**ntry of the ballroom, her worst fears were about to hap**pen: ny**lons torn and broken high heels. Her date was about to **nick el**ectrical wires sticking out from a light fixture, but Elise pulled him away at the last second.

18. One piece of candy costs 55¢, the other costs 20¢.

19. Mark averaged 328 pennies a day. To find the average, add the three different amounts of pennies together and divide by three.

20. Here's the trick: If the total of the digits of any number is divisible by three, then the number itself is divisible by three.

Molly added 73¢, 29¢, and 45¢, and the total was $1.47. If you add 1 + 4 + 7, the answer is 12. Twelve is divisible by three. Therefore, $1.47 is also divisible by three.

21. The answer is ten pennies, four nickels, and two dimes.

22. Here are fifteen words that can be made using the letters in the word *quarter*, but there are more! How many did you find?

rate	at	art	truer	err
ate	rare	ear	eat	rat
quart	tar	tear	tea	are

23. Here's one way the puzzle can be completed:

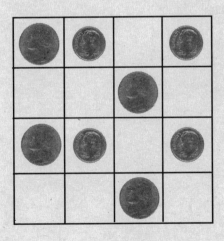

24. a. One is to five as dime is to *half-dollar*. (A dime is one fifth of a half-dollar.)

b. Two is to five as dime is to *quarter*. (Two and five have the same relationship as a dime has to a quarter. $10/25 = 2/5$.)

c. One is to five as penny is to *nickel*. (A penny is one fifth of a nickel.)

d. Five is to ten as Jefferson is to *Roosevelt*. (President Thomas Jefferson is on the nickel and President Franklin D. Roosevelt is on the dime.)

25. You would have 1¢. This puzzle is easiest to solve if it's done backward. One seventh of 70¢ is 10¢. One half of 10¢ is 5¢. One fifth of 5¢ is 1¢.

26. The chance that both coins are dimes is one in three. Let's take a look at the possibilities. (Remember — one of the coins is a dime.)

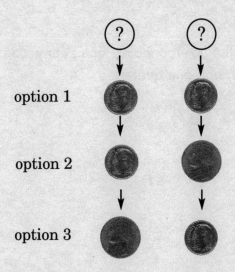

Out of the three possibilities, only one is of two dimes.

27. The two coins are a quarter and a dime. One of the coins is not a dime — but the other one is!

28. The answer is c, 36¢. Since there is an equal amount of nickels and pennies, the total amount must be divisible by six. Thirty-six cents is the only amount that is evenly divisible by six.

29. Believe it or not, you'd be a millionaire times ten if you opted for the second choice. By the thirtieth day, you'd have a whopping $10,737,418.23!

30. Martha has four coins: one penny, one nickel, one dime, and one quarter.

31. Here's how the coins should appear from left to right:

32. Andy has 2¢, which is the least amount of money.

Here's one way to look at it: If Andy and Brenda have 12¢ and Brenda and Curt have 18¢, then Curt must have 6¢ more than Andy. We also know that Andy and Curt have 10¢. That must mean that Curt has 8¢ and Andy has 2¢.

33. $1.50 was the most she could have earned (6 x 25¢). She lost 35¢ each time she didn't get an A (25¢ + 10¢). $1.50 less 70¢ (2 non-A's) equals 80¢. So Mindy received four A's.

34. Here's one way to do this. Can you find other ways?

1. Move 10 to 8.
2. Move 3 to 10.
3. Move 7 to 9.
4. Move 10 to 8.
5. Move 2 to 9.
6. Move 9 to 7.
7. Move 7 to 2.
8. Move 1 to 4.

35. The missing card should look like this:

The triangle and square stand for a dime and a quarter, which is the only combination of the four coins that isn't shown.

36. Eleven dimes were contributed.
One dollar and twenty-one cents is evenly divisible by eleven. If each student contributed 11¢, then there were eleven students in all. And since each student contributed the same two coins — a dime and a penny — then eleven dimes were contributed in all.

Answers to Challenging Coin Puzzles

37. Six.

This can happen in two different ways. Here are the seven possible combinations showing the different values for each pile. The two combinations showing the correct answer are underlined. Six is the smallest number in the biggest pile of any of the combinations

1, 2, 10	2, 3, 8	<u>3, 4, 6</u>
1, 3, 9	2, 4, 7	
1, 5, 7	<u>2, 5, 6</u>	

38. Put a penny in cup 1, a penny in cup 2, and two pennies in cup 3. Now put cup 2 inside cup 3 and you'll have an odd number of pennies in each cup!

39. 69¢ (One quarter, four dimes, and four pennies.)

40. Eight.

Here's a list of the different possibilities:

$$1¢ + 5¢ = 6¢ \qquad 5¢ + 5¢ = 10¢$$
$$1¢ + 10¢ = 11¢ \qquad 5¢ + 10¢ = 15¢$$
$$1¢ + 25¢ = 26¢ \qquad 5¢ + 25¢ = 30¢$$
$$25¢ + 25¢ = 50¢ \qquad 10¢ + 25¢ = 35¢$$

41. Four pennies.

Even if the mother gets three different-colored gumballs with the first three pennies, she will definitely get a match with the fourth penny!

42. Bob has a quarter and Bill has a dime.

One of the first two statements must be incorrect. Since one of those statements is false and we know that two of the three statements are false, that means that the third statement is false. Bob does not have a dime. If Bob doesn't have a dime, then he must have a quarter. Therefore, Bill has a dime.

43. Each received two coins.

Out for a walk was a grandmother, who is a daughter to her mother; the grandmother's daughter, who has a daughter and is therefore a daughter and a mom; and the daughter. This makes three people, two of whom are mothers and all three of whom are daughters.

44. Here's the answer:

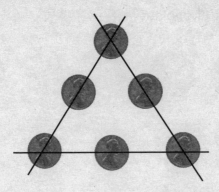

45. Marcia had three coins — one quarter, one dime, and one penny.

46. Pick any three coins to put on one side of the scale. Then put the other three coins on the other side of the scale.

Whichever side has the light coin will rise. Remove the three heavy coins from the other side of the scale so that you're left with three coins, including the light one.

Now pick any two coins from the remaining three. Place one coin on one side of the scale and one coin on the other side. If the scale balances perfectly, then the lightest coin is the one of the three you didn't place on the scale. Otherwise, whichever side rises holds the light coin.

47. Here's one way to solve this coin puzzle. Can you think of another?

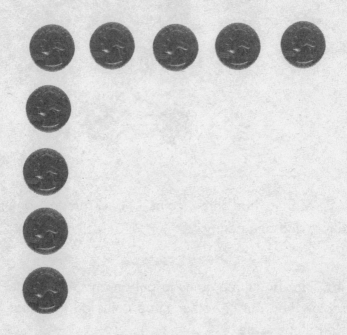

48. Here's how John came up with the answer. He looked at the beginning amount of money (1¢) and the end amount (20¢). He added those amounts together for a total of 21¢.

He then noticed that he could do the same for 2¢ and 19¢, and 3¢ and 18¢, and so on. He realized that there were ten pairs of money totals that equaled 21¢.

Twenty-one cents times ten is $2.10.